CW00672411

:ALTH

First Aid for M

Subject	Section	Page
Contents		1
What is mental health?	1	2
Identifying mental health conditions	2	8
Providing advice and starting a conversation	3	10
Stress	4	14
Drugs and alcohol	5	18
First aid action plan for mental health	6	24
Mental health in the workplace	7	28
Depression	8	34
Anxiety	9	44

Subject	Section	Page
Post-traumatic stress disorder (PTSD)	10	48
Self-harm	11	54
Suicide	12	60
Eating disorders	13	66
Personality disorders	14	72
Bipolar disorder	15	78
Psychosis	16	84
Schizophrenia	17	88
Mental health helplines	18	94

First Aid for Mental Health is published by: **Nuco Training Ltd**

WHAT IS MENTAL HEALTH?

One in four people will experience a mental health problem at some point in their lifetime.

While mental health problems are common, most are mild, tend to be short-term and can be successfully treated using professional therapies, medication, self-help techniques or a combination of these treatment methods.

Mental health is about how we think, feel and behave. Anxiety and depression are the most common mental health problems. They are often a reaction to a difficult life event, such as bereavement, but can also be caused by work-related issues.

Where work-related stress is prolonged, it can lead to both physical and psychological damage, including anxiety and depression. Work can also aggravate pre-existing conditions, and problems at work can bring on symptoms or make their effects worse.

Whether work is causing the health issue or aggravating it, employers have a legal responsibility to help their employees. Work-related mental health issues must be assessed to measure the levels of risk to staff. Where a risk is identified, steps must be taken to remove it, or reduce it as far as reasonably practicable.

Some employees will have a pre-existing physical or mental health condition when recruited or may develop one caused by factors that are not work-related factors.

Their employers may have further legal requirements, to make reasonable adjustments under equalities legislation.

FIRST AID FOR MENTAL HEALTH

First aid for mental health is the initial support provided to a person experiencing a mental health problem until professional help is received or until the crisis is resolved.

In 2017, the UK government commissioned Lord Stevenson and Paul Farmer *(Chief Executive of Mind)* to independently review the role employers can play to better support individuals with mental health conditions in the workplace.

The 'Thriving at Work' report sets out a framework of actions – called 'Core Standards' – that the reviewers recommend employers of all sizes can and should put in place. The core standards have been designed to help employers improve the mental health of their workplace and enable individuals with mental health conditions to thrive.

The aims of first aid for mental health:

- **Preserve life where a person could be a danger to themselves or others**
- **Alleviate suffering by providing immediate comfort and support**
- **Prevent the condition from developing into a more serious problem**
- **Promote recovery of good mental health by signposting and obtaining professional support**

Roles and responsibilities of the First Aider for Mental Health:

- The main point of contact for anyone who is going through some form of mental health problem
- Identifying the early signs and symptoms of mental ill health
- Start supportive conversations with people experiencing a mental health problem
- Listen non-judgementally and provide reassurance
- Assess the risk of self-harm and suicide
- To signpost and encourage appropriate professional support
- Reduce the stigma attached to mental health and promote awareness
- Summon for the appropriate emergency services if necessary
- To maintain confidentiality and provide an ongoing supportive working environment

The HSE's stance relating to First Aid Needs Assessment

MENTAL ILL HEALTH AND FIRST AID

Following your employers' first aid needs assessment, you may decide that it will be beneficial to have personnel trained to identify and understand symptoms and be able to support someone who might be experiencing a mental health issue.

You should consider ways to manage mental ill health in your workplace, which are appropriate for your business, such as providing information or training for managers and employees, employing occupational health professionals, appointing mental health trained First Aider's and implementing employee support programmes.

First aid training courses covering mental health, teach delegates how to recognise warning signs of mental ill health and help them to develop the skills and confidence to approach and support someone, while keeping themselves safe.

The impact of mental health issues:

- **Day-to-day:** Mental ill health can make it harder for people to cope with general day-to-day activities
- **Physical health:** Mental illness can impair the ability to protect and develop physical wellbeing
- **Work:** Obtaining or maintaining a job may be more difficult when symptoms of a mental health condition make it harder for someone to function normally
- **Education:** Studying may be more difficult when living with a mental health condition and often students do not reach their true potential
- **Driving:** Mental health conditions themselves do not stop people from driving. However, certain medications that the person may be taking, or if they are a risk to themselves and others, will influence the decision
- **Parenting & children:** Mental illness can affect relationships and family life. Certain medications can also have an affect on pregnancy, but there is now a wide range of medications that are safe to use during pregnancy, such as the antidepressant, sertraline
- **Stigma:** Stigma can create barriers for people to seek help for their mental health condition and can make their situation much worse

MENTAL HEALTH STIGMA

In the context of mental health, there are two main types of stigma:

Social stigma - Includes the negative attitudes and discriminatory behaviours that society or particular individuals hold towards those with mental health problems. A belief that *"all people with mental health problems are violent and dangerous"* could be an example of social stigma.

Self-stigma - This is where people with mental health problems believe what is being said about their condition and agree with their viewpoints. Self-stigma can result in delays or the avoidance of seeking help for their condition due to the fear of being rejected or humiliated.

The effects of stigma

There are a number of adverse effects caused by stigma, including:

- **Feelings of shame and hopelessness**
- **Reluctance to ask anyone for help or to seek professional treatment**
- **Victimisation, harassment and physical violence**
- **Difficulties finding employment and taking part in activities**
- **Lack of understanding from family and friends**
- **Developing a practice of self-stigmatisation caused by the social stigma**

Coping with stigma

No individual should have to tolerate others treating them differently because of a mental health condition. People can help to combat stigma by:

- **Seeking professional help - not letting the fear of being 'labelled' with a mental illness stop this**
- **Showing family and friends reliable information to improve their understanding**
- **Not equating themselves with their condition**
- **Joining a support group to talk about stigma and relate to others**
- **Organising local campaigns or getting involved with national campaigns about mental health**

MENTAL HEALTH STATISTICS

- Approximately 1 billion people worldwide suffer from a mental disorder [1]
- Lost productivity as a result of two of the most common mental disorders, anxiety and depression, costs the global economy US$ 1 trillion each year [1]
- Approximately 1 in 4 people in the UK will experience a mental health problem each year [2]
- An estimated 1 in 6 adults experience a 'common mental health disorder' like depression or anxiety in any given week in England [3]
- The NHS in England spent £14.3 billion on mental health services in 2020/21 - 14.8% of local NHS funding allocations [3]

References:
1. Mental health matters (The Lancet Global Health, www.thelancet.com, 2020)
2. Mental health facts and statistics (Mind, 2017)
3. Mental health statistics, England (Commons Library Research Briefing, 2021)

THE MENTAL HEALTH CONTINUUM MODEL

Mental health does not simply mean the absence of a mental illness – it is possible to have good mental wellbeing whilst living with a diagnosed mental illness. In contrast, someone who has no diagnosable mental illness can still have a low level of mental wellbeing.

EXCELLENT LEVEL OF MENTAL WELLBEING

A PERSON WHO EXPERIENCES AN EXCELLENT LEVEL OF MENTAL WELLBEING, REGARDLESS OF BEING DIAGNOSED WITH A MENTAL ILLNESS

A PERSON WHO EXPERIENCES AN EXCELLENT LEVEL OF MENTAL WELLBEING AND HAS NO MENTAL ILLNESS

CLINICAL DIAGNOSIS

NO DIAGNOSIS

A PERSON WHO HAS BEEN DIAGNOSED WITH A MENTAL ILLNESS AND ALSO EXPERIENCES A LOW LEVEL OF MENTAL WELLBEING

A PERSON WHO HAS NO DIAGNOSABLE MENTAL ILLNESS BUT ALSO HAS A LOW LEVEL OF MENTAL WELLBEING

LOW LEVEL OF MENTAL WELLBEING

The mental health risk factors:

- Discrimination and stigma
- Social isolation or loneliness
- Abuse, trauma or neglect
- Social disadvantage or financial troubles
- Unemployment or losing a job
- Having a long-term physical health condition or injury
- Severe or long-term stress
- Poverty or homelessness
- Being a long-term carer
- Drug or alcohol abuse
- Domestic violence
- Significant trauma as an adult, such as military combat
- The death of a loved one

THE EARLY WARNING SIGNS OF A MENTAL HEALTH PROBLEM.

Could include:

- Losing interest in activities and hobbies that were previously enjoyed
- Underperforming at work with no apparent explanation
- Increased anxiety levels, feeling exhausted and restless
- Isolating themselves and not wanting to socialise with friends and family
- Changes in appetite such as skipping meals or over-eating/bingeing
- Changes in perception such as hearing or seeing things that others don't
- Self-harming behaviour. Signs of cuts or bruising to uncommon areas of the body
- Reduced, or increased sex drive depending on the mental health problem

HOW TO START A CONVERSATION ABOUT MENTAL HEALTH

Starting a conversation can help tackle the stigma surrounding mental health and make the individual aware that they are not alone – mental health problems are very common and can be treated.

Think carefully about what you want to say before starting the conversation and make sure you are in the right environment without interruptions.

Avoid closed questions which only require a 'yes' or 'no' answer.

Ask open questions such as *"How are you feeling?"* This should provide a basis for a more detailed response.

One of the most important things to do is listen to them carefully without personal judgement. Listening to what the person tells you can sometimes be difficult to hear, so you need to allow time for reflection.

You can provide advice and signpost to professional help but ultimately the individual will need to act for themselves. The exception is when they are in crisis, then you can assist them to seek further help, or call the emergency services if they are a danger to themselves and to others.

WHAT IS NON-JUDGEMENTAL LISTENING?

Non-judgemental listening is when you listen to what someone is telling you with your undivided attention and truly show an interest in what the person is trying to say.

Everybody has different opinions and it is natural to judge what the person is telling you, but you must keep these opinions to yourself and communicate with the person empathetically, without displaying any form of personal judgement.

Non-judgemental listening is not just about listening, the term includes both non-verbal and verbal communication skills.

Here are some points to consider for non-judgemental listening:

- **Give them plenty of time to talk and do not interrupt**
- **Listen carefully to the words spoken**
- **Allow time for reflection**
- **Maintain eye contact but do not stare at the person**
- **Express empathy and do not judge the person**
- **Be aware of your tone of voice and volume level when speaking**
- **Keep an open body position, arms and legs uncrossed**
- **Once they have finished speaking, relay and summarise what they have told you**

Say less. Listen more.

WHEN AND WHO TO CONTACT FOR FURTHER HELP

If a person is in a state of crisis, you may need to seek help for them. This could be from a trusted friend or family member, or a healthcare professional.

The level of help required will depend on their current condition.

Who to contact:

- **Close friend or family member**
  A close friend or family member could be called who knows the person well and can offer them comfort and support

- **Crisis Line** *(if they are already assigned to a healthcare professional)*

- **The Samaritans** *(116 123)*
  The Samaritans operate a free to call service 24 hours a day, 365 days a year, if they want to talk to someone in confidence

- **NHS**
  You can call NHS 111, or visit www.111.nhs.uk or www.nhs24.scot (Scotland), if you or someone you know requires urgent care, but it is not life-threatening, such as experiencing a mental health problem for the first time. Alternatively, contact your GP practice and ask for an emergency appointment.

When you should contact the emergency services.

A mental health emergency should be taken as seriously as a medical emergency.

Call 999 or go directly to A&E if they are:

- **Experiencing serious suicidal thoughts and feelings**
- **Thinking about harming themselves or someone else**
- **Experiencing symptoms of an acute underlying medical condition**
- **They have already hurt themselves**

It is important to note that some people may decline help and they cannot be forced to go to A&E. It is fairly common for people to have suicidal thoughts that come and go and they may never act on them. The situation at the time of crisis should give you an indication of the level of support required.

HOW A FIRST AIDER CAN TAKE CARE OF THEIR OWN HEALTH AND EMOTIONS

Supporting others who are experiencing mental health problems can affect your own mental health and wellbeing.

Ideally, employers should factor in first aid for mental health to their policies and procedures to protect you as a First Aider and ensure the role does not affect your main responsibilities in the workplace.

- Speak to your employer or manager about any concerns you may have
- If your own mental health is being affected, seek support from a professional
- Try not to get too involved – your role is to identify the warning signs, provide immediate support and signpost towards professional help
- Make sure you take time out for yourself and look after your own physical and mental wellbeing

Stress is the *"adverse reaction people have to excessive pressure or other types of demand placed on them". (HSE)*

WHAT HAPPENS TO THE BODY WHEN SOMEONE IS STRESSED?

Adrenal gland produces adrenaline:

This speeds up the heart and increases blood pressure.

Adrenal gland produces cortisol:

This increases glucose in the blood and energy production. Over long periods of stress these reactions can cause illness and reduce life expectancy.

The pituitary gland produces oxytocin:

This can reverse the effects of stress.

Stress affects people differently – what stresses one person may not affect another. Factors like skills and experience, age or disability may all affect whether someone can cope.

Causes of stress include:

- Work
- Relationships
- Bereavement
- Moving house
- Finances
- Poor physical health
- Divorce
- Bullying
- Family and friends
- Poor behaviour
- Travel
- Personal issues

THE EMOTIONAL, PHYSICAL AND BEHAVIOURAL EFFECTS OF STRESS.

How someone may feel mentally and emotionally:

- Anxious
- Angry
- Lack of concentration
- Difficulty making decisions
- Low self-esteem
- Sad
- Frustrated
- Overwhelmed
- Constant worrying
- Racing thoughts

How someone may feel physically:

- Headaches
- Chest pain
- Tiredness
- Nausea
- Muscle tension
- Dizziness

Behavioural effects:

- Outbursts of anger
- Undereating or overeating
- Changes in sex drive
- Restlessness
- Social withdrawal
- Exercising less often than usual

THE LONG-TERM EFFECTS OF STRESS

Lots of things can cause someone to be stressed and generally, this isn't something to be concerned about. However, the effects of long-term stress can put their health at risk.

The long-term effects of stress can include:

- Stress can lead to mental health conditions such as depression, anxiety and personality disorders
- Cardiovascular problems such as high blood pressure, heart disease and stroke
- Problems with the immune system, lower resistance to infection and skin conditions
- Digestive problems such as appetite loss, stomach ulcers, vomiting and diarrhoea
- Excessive changes in behaviour such as alcohol and substance misuse

Coping strategies for stress.

- Realise when stress is becoming a problem and identify the underlying causes
- Build emotional strength and re-organise lifestyle to tackle the causes
- Eat a healthy diet, avoid skipping meals and try to adopt regular eating patterns
- Make time to relax and socialise with friends and family
- Set goals or challenges to help build confidence
- Avoid unhealthy habits such as smoking or excessive alcohol consumption
- Helping other people can relieve stress and help to put problems into perspective
- Look for the positives in life, rather than the causes of stress

When we refer to substance misuse, we mean the use of drugs or alcohol at levels that could cause harm.

"Substance abuse (or misuse) refers to the harmful or hazardous use of psychoactive substances, including alcohol and illicit drugs".

Reference: World Health Organisation

The four main categories of drugs are:

- **Stimulants** *(e.g. cocaine, ecstasy etc.)*
- **Depressants** *(e.g. alcohol, cannabis etc.)*
- **Opiates** *(e.g. heroin, codeine etc.)*
- **Hallucinogens** *(e.g. LSD, magic mushrooms etc.)*

ALCOHOL MISUSE AND THE LOWER RISK DRINKING LIMITS RECOMMENDED BY THE NHS

Alcohol misuse means drinking excessively – more than the 'lower risk limits' of alcohol consumption.

A unit of alcohol is 10ml of pure alcohol, which is equivalent to half a pint of lower to normal-strength lager *(ABV 3.6%)*.

A small glass *(125ml)* of wine contains about 1.5 units of alcohol.

Lower-risk limits:

Not regularly drinking more than 14 units of alcohol a week.

If someone drinks as much as 14 units a week, it's best to spread this evenly over 3 or more days.

THE RISKS AND CONTRAINDICATIONS OF DRINKING ALCOHOL WHILE TAKING PRESCRIBED MEDICATION

Drinking alcohol while taking prescribed medication, including antidepressants is generally not advised.

Alcohol can reduce the effectiveness of some medications and intensify the possible side effects. Because of this, it is best to avoid drinking alcohol if the person is taking medication such as antidepressants.

Contraindications may include:

- **Exacerbate the symptoms of illness**
- **Reduce the effectiveness of the medication**
- **Nausea, vomiting and headaches**
- **Drowsiness and dizziness**
- **Changes in blood pressure**
- **Increased risk of accidents**

WHAT SELF-MEDICATING MEANS AND THE POSSIBLE RISKS TO OUR MENTAL HEALTH

'Self-medicating' is when someone uses alcohol, illegal drugs or prescription drugs as a coping mechanism to relieve symptoms of sadness and not being able to cope. Alcohol is one of the most common substances used because it is legal in the UK and easy to obtain.

While self-medicating may provide immediate relief of symptoms such as anxiety, this is only temporary. Alcohol and other drugs can adversely change the chemistry of the brain, which can exacerbate the symptoms of mental illness. Substance misuse can also lead to addiction and cause serious harm to a person's physical wellbeing.

When someone has been diagnosed with a mental illness and has a subsequent alcohol/drug misuse problem, this is known as 'dual diagnosis'. Substance misuse is more prevalent among people with severe mental health illnesses.

Recreational drugs *(including alcohol)* can be harmful to the body in many ways. Drugs can affect the way people perceive things around them, their behaviour and their physical and mental health, both in the short and long-term.

The short-term adverse effects of using recreational substances may include:

- **Impaired judgement**
- **Mood swings**
- **Feelings of anxiety and depression**
- **Paranoia**
- **Confusion**
- **Memory problems**
- **Altered perception of reality**

Mental health problems can develop in someone who uses recreational substances regularly or, someone with an undiagnosed mental health problem might use recreational drugs to alleviate their symptoms.

There is a high risk that this will make their condition worse, or make them believe the substance misuse is the cause of their mental ill health.

Mental health problems can be improved if someone reduces or stops taking drugs for a reasonable amount of time. In all cases, whether they are a 'weekend user', or if they are dependent on the substance, providing initial support and signposting to a professional is the first step in helping someone improve their mental health and wellbeing.

Long-term adverse effects may include:

- **Mental health problems**
- **Addiction/dependency**
- **Social problems**
- **Heart and liver disease**
- **Cancers**
- **Severe withdrawal symptoms**

The first aid procedure for drug and alcohol misuse:

- Stay calm and be reassuring
- Sit them down in a quiet room where they feel comfortable
- Stay with them and talk to them compassionately
- Listen to what they say without judgement and make eye contact
- Try to find out what they are taking *(or have taken)*. **The emergency services will need this information if they start to feel seriously unwell**
- Don't make assumptions
- Be patient with them
- Once their current condition improves, assist and signpost to professional support such as their GP, if this is appropriate

If they are under the influence, make sure they are safe. If they start to feel physically unwell such as having difficulties breathing, or if they are experiencing serious suicidal emotions, call NHS 111 for advice or 999 in an emergency.

THE TREATMENTS AVAILABLE TO HELP SOMEONE WITH A DRUG OR ALCOHOL PROBLEM

If drug or alcohol misuse is affecting someone's mental health, they could:

- Visit their GP in the first instance
- See their local NHS drug and alcohol treatment service
- Contact a drug and alcohol treatment organisation

Talking treatments:

Psychological therapies are available for individuals who have drug and alcohol problems, such as cognitive behavioural therapy *(CBT)*. Other treatment options consist of medication, detoxification *(detox)* and self-help techniques.

SIGNPOSTING FOR DRUGS AND ALCOHOL

Adfam
adfam.org.uk
Support and information for family and friends for people with drug or alcohol problems.

Alcoholics Anonymous
alcoholics-anonymous.org.uk
National network of local alcoholics to help recover from alcoholism.

Drinkaware
drinkaware.co.uk
Aims to reduce alcohol misuse and harm.

DrugWise
drugwise.org.uk
Provides drug information which is topical, evidence-based and non-judgemental.

Frank
talktofrank.com
Offers free confidential drug information and advice 24 hours a day.

We Are With You
wearewithyou.org.uk
Services for people who are dependent on drugs and alcohol, and their families.

C   Check for significant risk of suicide or harm

A   Apply non-judgemental communication skills

R   Reassure and provide information

E   Encourage professional support and self-help strategies

C.A.R.E. –

CHECK for significant risk of suicide or harm

The first step in helping someone who is suffering from a mental health problem is to look for signs of significant distress including suicidal thoughts and emotions.

Indicators of suicidal thoughts and emotions may include:

- Telling you they want their life to end
- Threatening to hurt or kill themselves
- Speaking or writing about death, dying or suicide
- Feelings of hopelessness and saying negative things about themselves
- Withdrawing from family, friends and society
- Apparent mood swings and acting recklessly
- Becoming very anxious, irritable and stressed
- An increase in the use of alcohol and drugs

When someone is in immediate danger to themselves and to others, or they are actively suicidal, dial 999 for an ambulance or go directly to the nearest A&E department.

For non life-threatening emergencies, there are a number of options available to support the person, or for the person to seek the support themselves.

This includes *(but not limited to)*:

- A trusted friend or family member
- Samaritans – 116 123
- Their GP – book an emergency appointment
- NHS – 111

C.A.R.E. –

APPLY non-judgemental communication skills

- Let the person tell you how they are feeling and listen to what they are saying with your full attention

- Give them time and have patience. If they pause their response, wait a few seconds as they may not have finished what they are trying to say

- Maintain eye contact, keep an open body position and be aware of your tone of voice when speaking

- Use open-ended questions to continue the discussion and avoid closed questions with 'yes' or 'no' answers

- Repeat back what they have told you. This demonstrates to the individual you have been listening and they have your undivided attention

C.A.R.E. –
REASSURE and provide information

Let the person know that they have done the right thing in telling you and reassure them that with the right support, they should feel better soon.

- Let them know you care for them and remind them that they are not alone – one in four adults experience similar problems
- Let the person know it is okay to talk about their feelings and reassure them that you are there to listen to whatever they want to say or discuss
- Show gratitude to the person for sharing their feelings and acknowledge the courage it has taken to talk
- Do not try to diagnose or make assumptions about their condition – provide reassurance and information

If you believe the person could be in immediate danger, remain calm and stay with them until professional help has been arranged.

C.A.R.E. –
ENCOURAGE self-help strategies

- Individuals can help themselves personally through self-help techniques and making simple changes to their lifestyle
- Some people may find that self-help techniques are really helping them feel better without professional involvement. However, it is important to note that recovering from a mental health illness can take time and dedication. Very often, self-help techniques are used in conjunction with professional therapies
- 'Guided self-help' involves working through a self-help workbook or computer course with the support of a therapist. Psychological therapies, including guided self-help are available through the NHS

Being mentally healthy should be important to each and every one of us. Although there are many professional support strategies available, self-help can make a huge difference in helping someone manage and improve their mental health.

Self-help advice can include:

- Being active and exercising regularly
- Getting enough sleep
- Maintaining a healthy diet
- Socialising and connecting with others
- Self-help books and resources
- Relaxation and mindfulness techniques
- Avoiding drugs and alcohol
- Peer support groups

FACTORS WHICH CAN AFFECT MENTAL HEALTH IN THE WORKPLACE

Mental health problems can develop outside and inside of the workplace. There are several internal factors which can have a negative impact on a person's mental health and make it harder to cope.

Factors can include:

- **Unmanageable workloads, long hours and increasing pressures**
- **Lack of control over work and poor supervision from management**
- **Bullying, stigmatisation and bad relationships with peers**
- **Lack of involvement when the workplace is undergoing change**
- **Inadequate pay, problems receiving pay and lack of reward and recognition**
- **Dangerous or poor physical working environments**
- **Traumatic experiences**

LEGISLATION AND GUIDANCE RELATING TO MENTAL HEALTH IN THE WORKPLACE

National Institute for Health and Care Excellence - nice.org.uk
Produces and publicises evidence-based guidance and quality standards to support the identification, treatment and management of mental health conditions.

Health and Safety Executive (HSE) - hse.gov.uk
The independent regulators of work-related health, safety and illness in Great Britain. The HSE produces guidance and publications relating to workplace health, safety and welfare.

Health and Safety at Work Act 1974
The primary piece of legislation covering workplace health and safety. The Act imposes a duty on employers to ensure the health, safety and welfare at work of all their employees.

Mental Health Act 1983
Covers the assessment, treatment and rights of people with mental health disorders. The Act states when someone should be detained and treated in hospital, without consent *(known as 'being sectioned')*.

Mental Capacity Act 2005
Designed to protect and empower people who may lack the mental capacity to make their own decisions about their care and treatment. It applies to people aged 16 and over.

It covers decisions about day-to-day things like what to wear or what to buy for the weekly shop, or serious life-changing decisions like whether to move into a care home or have major surgery.

Equality Act 2010

The Equality Act legally protects people from discrimination in the workplace when accessing services, and in the wider society. It replaced previous anti-discrimination laws with a single Act, making the law easier to understand and strengthening protection in some situations. It sets out the different ways in which it is unlawful to treat an individual.

Data Protection Act 2018

The Data Protection Act stipulates how organisations should deal with personal information if it is on a computer or in writing. It is a national law which complements the European Union's General Data Protection Regulation *(GDPR)*. All personal information should be kept up-to-date and confidentiality of the information is a key part of maintaining dignity, especially for those using health and social care services.

Human Rights Act 1998

The Human Rights Act enables people to defend their rights in UK courts and obliges public organisations to treat everyone equally, with fairness, dignity and respect. It enables individuals to enforce 16 of the fundamental rights and freedoms contained in the European Convention on Human Rights *(ECHR)*.

HSE work-related statistics 2021/22

- **914,000 workers suffering from work-related stress, depression or anxiety**
- **The effects of the coronavirus pandemic were found to be a major contributory factor to work-related stress, depression or anxiety**
- **372,000 workers suffering from a new case of work-related stress, depression or anxiety**
- **17.0 million working days lost due to work-related stress, depression or anxiety**
- **Stress, depression or anxiety accounted for 51% of all work-related ill health cases**

Reference: Health and Safety Executive (HSE) - Summary statistics for Great Britain 2022

HOW EMPLOYERS CAN BUILD A POSITIVE MENTAL HEALTH CULTURE IN THE WORKPLACE

Good mental health and wellbeing is one of the most valuable assets to any organisation. Here are some steps employers can take to improve the mental health culture of the workplace.

Employers can build a positive mental health culture by:

- Developing a mental health action plan and implementing an effective mental health policy
- Providing mental health training including specific first aid for mental health training for employees across all levels of the organisation and adjusting job roles to accommodate new responsibility
- Publicising the organisation's commitment to mental health, as with environmental commitments
- Evaluating the possible causes of mental ill health in the workplace and signifying areas which need improvement. This could include the analysis of absence and performance data
- Ensuring employers and senior management spend more time communicating and getting to know employees. This should make it easier to talk about mental health and to identify when employees may need a helping hand
- Monitoring employee performance and providing recognition and reward for achievements
- Introducing networks, initiatives and activities involving mental health and communicating this via the company's intranet, news bulletins and workplace communal areas
- Offering occupational health services, return to work schemes, employee assistance programmes and allowing flexible working hours to help employees meet their responsibilities outside of the workplace
- Make employees feel valued by involving them in decision making and managing their own workloads

HOW EMPLOYEES CAN BUILD A POSITIVE MENTAL HEALTH CULTURE IN THE WORKPLACE

- Educate yourself on mental health and wellbeing and participate in workplace initiatives
- Make effort to talk to your colleagues and ask them how they are feeling. Take on little tasks to help make their life easier during tough times
- Don't be afraid to talk to someone about your own thoughts and feelings and ask for help when you need it
- Challenge workplace 'politics' and speak to a manager if something is not quite right
- Show an interest in your colleague's opinions, cultures and beliefs
- Build friendships with your colleagues and organise to meet up outside of the working environment
- Make the most out of your lunch break – eat healthily, read a book, listen to music or take a stroll
- Set a challenge by organising charity events for good causes amongst your colleagues
- Take a break every once-in-a-while and make the most out of your annual leave
- Time is precious - ensure you have a good work-life balance and don't overdo it. Make time for your family and friends outside of the workplace
- Make sure you have a good sleep pattern and listen to what your body is telling you

The impact of a positive mental health culture:

- Increased awareness of mental health
- Employees more likely to disclose their problems
- Improved relationships amongst peers
- Increased job satisfaction and happiness
- Improved productivity, teamwork and staff morale
- Better decision making and employee involvement
- Attracting new job talent
- Enhanced business reputation
- Reduced absence and staff turnover
- Reduced business costs

What can we do to help ourselves?

- Spend quality time with family and friends
- Exercise regularly
- Eat and maintain a healthy diet
- Get enough sleep
- Read books or listen to audiobooks
- Listen to your favourite music
- Learn a new skill
- Start gardening
- Take up a hobby or join a club
- Take a break/holiday
- Volunteer for the community
- Meditation and mindfulness techniques
- Visit your GP if you have any physical or mental health concerns

THE FIVE STEPS TO MENTAL WELLBEING AS RECOMMENDED BY THE NHS

This information is what the NHS recommends based on evidence and research.

We can improve our wellbeing by building these five steps into our day-to-day lives. If you give them a try, you may feel happier, more positive and able to get the most from life.

Connect...
Connect with the people around you; your family, friends, colleagues and neighbours. Spend time developing these relationships.

Be active...
You don't have to go to the gym. Take a walk, go cycling or play a game of football. Find an activity that you enjoy and make it a part of your life.

Keep learning...
Learning a new skill can give you a sense of achievement and a new confidence. So why not sign up for that cooking course, start learning to play a musical instrument, or figure out how to fix your bike?

Give to others...
Even the smallest act can count, whether it's a smile, a thank you or a kind word. Larger acts, such as volunteering at your local community centre, can improve your mental wellbeing and help you build new social networks.

Be mindful...
Be more aware of the present moment, including your thoughts and feelings, your body and the world around you. Some people call this awareness *"mindfulness"*. It can positively change the way you feel about life and how you approach challenges.

You can visit the NHS mood zone for further information on the five steps to mental wellbeing: https://www.nhs.uk/conditions/stress-anxiety-depression/

DEPRESSION

Depression is when someone feels persistently sad and unhappy for a long period of time and affects their everyday life. Depression can sometimes be viewed as trivial and not a real health condition - this is not true. Depression is a real illness with real symptoms and is a very common mental health condition.

The severity of depression is usually categorised into the following:

- **Mild depression** – has some impact on daily life
- **Moderate depression** – has a significant impact on daily life
- **Severe depression** – makes it almost impossible to get through daily life

There are several types of depression and the condition itself can be a resulting symptom of a mental illness such as bipolar disorder.

- **Postnatal depression** – women can develop depression a short time after giving birth; this is known as postnatal depression and it is treated in a similar way to other types of depression - with talking therapies and antidepressant medicines
- **Seasonal affective disorder** – a type of depression with a seasonal pattern, usually related to winter. Coincidentally, this condition is also known as *"winter depression"*
- **Bipolar disorder** – with bipolar disorder there are spells of both depression and excessively high mood (mania); the depressive symptoms are similar to that of clinical depression *(See Page 78)*

SIGNS AND SYMPTOMS OF DEPRESSION:

- Avoiding contact with family and friends
- Avoiding social events and neglecting hobbies
- Not doing as well at work
- Continuous low mood, feeling upset and tearful
- Feeling hopeless and low self-esteem
- Lack of motivation or interest in things
- Feeling irritable and intolerant of other people
- Thoughts of self-harm or suicide
- Changes in appetite or weight loss/gain
- Lack of energy, muscle aches and pains
- Disturbed sleep patterns and low sex drive

Some causes of depression:

Stressful events

Most people take time to come to terms with stressful events, such as bereavement or a relationship breakdown. When these stressful events occur, the risk of becoming depressed is increased. Particularly if the person stops seeing their friends and family and tries to deal with problems on their own.

Personality

A person may be more vulnerable to depression if they have certain personality traits, such as low self-esteem or being overly self-critical. This may be because of the genes they've inherited from their parents, their early life experiences, or both.

Family history

If someone's family member has had depression in the past, such as a parent, sister or brother, it's more likely that they'll also develop it.

Giving birth

Some women are particularly vulnerable to depression after pregnancy. The hormonal and physical changes, as well as the added responsibility of a new life, can lead to postnatal depression.

Loneliness

Becoming cut off from family and friends can increase the risk of depression.

Alcohol and drugs

When life is getting them down, some people try to cope by drinking too much alcohol or taking drugs. This can result in a spiral of depression.

Cannabis can help people relax, but there's evidence that it can also bring on depression, particularly in teenagers.

"Drowning your sorrows" with a drink is also not recommended. Alcohol is categorised as a *"strong depressant"*, which actually makes depression worse.

Illness

Someone may have a higher risk of depression if they have a longstanding or life-threatening illness, such as coronary heart disease or cancer.

Head injuries are also an often under-recognised cause of depression. A severe head injury can trigger mood swings and emotional problems.

Some people may have an underactive thyroid *(hypothyroidism)* resulting from problems with their immune system. In rarer cases, a minor head injury can damage the pituitary gland, which is a pea-sized gland at the base of the brain that produces thyroid-stimulating hormones.

This can cause numerous symptoms including extreme tiredness, and a lack of interest in sex (loss of libido), which can in turn lead to depression.

FIRST AID FOR DEPRESSION:

- Provide opportunity for the person to talk. If the person does not initiate a conversation with you, you should say something to them
- Choose an appropriate time where you will both feel comfortable, without any distractions
- Listen to them carefully, remain calm and provide reassurance
- Accept what they say without judging them and show your understanding
- Gently encourage them to help themselves – for example, by staying physically active, eating a balanced diet and doing things they enjoy
- If they feel comfortable, you can help them access information and resources
- Assist and signpost to professional support such as their GP, if this is appropriate

TREATMENT

Treatment for depression usually involves a combination of self-help, talking therapies and medicines.

The treatment that will be recommended will be based on the type of depression the person may have.

Mild depression

If they have mild depression, the following treatments may be recommended.

Wait and see

If their GP diagnoses them with mild depression, they may suggest waiting a short time to see if it gets better by itself. In this case, they'll be seen again by their GP after 2 weeks to monitor their progress. This is known as watchful waiting.

Exercise

There's evidence that exercise can help depression, and it's one of the main treatments for mild depression. They may be referred to a group exercise class.

Self-help

Talking through their feelings can be helpful. They could talk to a friend or relative, or they could ask their GP or local psychological therapies service if there are any self-help groups for people with depression in their area.

They could try self-help books or online cognitive behavioural therapy *(CBT)*.

Mental health apps

They can also find mental health apps and tools in the NHS apps library.

Mild to moderate depression

If someone has mild to moderate depression that isn't improving, or moderate depression, they may find a talking therapy helpful.

There are different types of talking therapies for depression, including cognitive behavioural therapy *(CBT)* and counselling.

Their GP can refer them for talking treatment, or they can refer themselves directly to a psychological therapies service.

Treatment continued...

Moderate to severe depression

If someone has moderate to severe depression, the following treatments may be recommended.

Antidepressants

Antidepressants are tablets that treat the symptoms of depression. There are almost 30 different types of antidepressant.

They have to be prescribed by a doctor, usually for depression that's moderate or severe.

Combination therapy

The person's GP may recommend that they take a course of antidepressants plus talking therapy, particularly if their depression is quite severe.

A combination of an antidepressant and CBT usually works better than having just one of these treatments.

Mental health teams

If someone has severe depression, they may be referred to a mental health team made up of psychologists, psychiatrists, specialist nurses and occupational therapists.

These teams often provide intensive specialist talking treatments as well as prescribed medication.

TALKING TREATMENTS

Cognitive behavioural therapy *(CBT)*

Cognitive behavioural therapy *(CBT)* aims to help people understand their thoughts and behaviour, and how they affect them.

CBT recognises that events in their past may have shaped them, but it concentrates mostly on how they can change the way they think, feel and behave in the present.

It teaches people how to overcome negative thoughts – for example, being able to challenge hopeless feelings.

CBT is available on the NHS for people with depression or any other mental health problem it's been shown to help.

It normally consists of a short course of sessions, usually 6 to 8 sessions, over 10 to 12 weeks on a one-to-one basis with a counsellor trained in CBT. In some cases, the counsellor may offer group CBT.

Online CBT

Online CBT is a type of CBT delivered through a computer, rather than face-to-face with a therapist.

It usually consists of a series of weekly sessions with the support of a healthcare professional.

Interpersonal therapy *(IPT)*

Interpersonal therapy *(IPT)* focuses on relationships with others and problems someone may be having in their relationships, such as difficulties with communication or coping with bereavement.

There's some evidence that IPT can be as effective as antidepressants or CBT, but more research is needed.

Psychodynamic psychotherapy

In psychodynamic (psychoanalytic) psychotherapy, a psychoanalytic therapist will encourage the individual to say whatever is going through their mind.

This will help them become aware of hidden meanings or patterns in what they do or say that may be contributing to their problems.

Counselling

Counselling is a form of therapy that helps people think about the problems they're experiencing in their life so they can find new ways of dealing with them.

Counsellors support people in finding solutions to problems, but don't tell them what to do.

Counselling on the NHS usually consists of 6 to 12 sessions that last an hour. They talk in confidence to a counsellor, who supports them and offers practical advice.

It's ideal for people who are generally healthy but need help coping with a current crisis, such as anger, relationship issues, bereavement, redundancy, infertility or a serious illness.

GETTING HELP

People should see their GP for more information about accessing NHS talking treatments. They can refer them for local talking treatments for depression.

People also have the option of self-referral. This means that if they prefer not to talk to their GP, they can go directly to a psychological therapies service.

SIGNPOSTING FOR DEPRESSION

Breathing Space
www.breathingspace.scot
A free, confidential phone and web based service for people in Scotland experiencing low mood, depression or anxiety.

Depression UK
depressionuk.org
A self-help organisation made up of individuals and local groups.

Mental Health Foundation
mentalhealth.org.uk
Provides information and support for anyone with mental health problems or learning disabilities.

Mind
mind.org.uk
Promotes the views and needs of people with mental health problems.

NHS Choices
nhs.uk
Provides a wealth of information on treatments for depression available through the NHS.

Samaritans
samaritans.org
A 24-hour telephone helpline for people struggling to cope.

SAMH - Scottish Association for Mental Health
www.samh.org.uk
Provides a range of mental health support and services.

Anxiety is a normal body response and we all experience feelings of anxiety. However, some people find it hard to control their worries. Their feelings of anxiety are more constant and can often affect their daily lives.

In cases such as this, the condition is commonly diagnosed as '**Generalised Anxiety Disorder (GAD)**'.

GAD is a common condition affecting approximately 5% of the UK population.

Anxiety is the main symptom of several conditions, including:

- **Panic disorder**
- **Phobias – such as claustrophobia**
- **Post-traumatic stress disorder** *(PTSD)*
- **Acute stress disorder**

The types of anxiety disorder:

- **Generalised anxiety disorder** *(GAD)*
  When a person struggles with raised anxiety and worry on a daily basis, which can be mild or severe

- **Panic disorder**
  An anxiety disorder where people regularly have sudden attacks of panic or fear.
  For someone with a panic disorder, feelings of anxiety, stress and panic occur regularly and at any time, often for no apparent reason

- **Acute stress disorder**
  This can develop shortly after a traumatic event causing significant anxiety and flashbacks. Symptoms usually subside within 3-4 weeks

- **Post-traumatic stress disorder**
  Similar to an 'acute stress disorder' but the symptoms persist for much longer, significantly affecting a person's day-to-day life

- **Phobias**
  An overwhelming and debilitating fear of an object, place, situation, feeling or animal. They develop when a person has an exaggerated or unrealistic sense of danger about a situation or object

The signs and symptoms of anxiety:

- **Feeling tense and unable to relax**
- **A sense of dread and feeling constantly 'on edge'**
- **Irritability and difficulties concentrating**
- **Social withdrawal**
- **Seeking lots of reassurance from others**
- **Dizziness and tiredness**
- **Strong, fast or irregular heartbeat**
- **Trembling or shaking**
- **Excessive sweating and shortness of breath**
- **Lack of energy, muscle aches and pains**
- **Dry mouth, feeling sick and headaches**
- **Panic attacks**

The first aid procedure for anxiety:

- Provide opportunity for the person to talk. If the person does not initiate a conversation with you, you should say something to them

- Choose an appropriate time where you will both feel comfortable, without distractions

- If the person is experiencing symptoms of a panic attack, suggest a change in location where they will feel more comfortable

- Encourage them to breathe slowly, in through their nose and out through their mouth

- Provide reassurance and be caring in your approach. Try to focus on positive points

- Listen to them carefully, remain calm and provide reassurance that they will feel better soon

- Accept what they say without judging them and show your understanding of their situation

- If they feel comfortable, you can help them access information and resources

- Assist and signpost to professional support such as their GP, if this is appropriate

THE TREATMENTS AVAILABLE TO HELP SOMEONE WITH ANXIETY.

Self-help techniques

Mindfulness, regular exercise, healthy foods, relaxing, reading, writing, meditation, avoiding caffeine, alcohol and smoking.

Cognitive behavioural therapy *(CBT)*

CBT is one of the most effective treatments for anxiety disorders and helps people question their negative or anxious thoughts and do things they would usually avoid because they make them feel anxious.

Antidepressants

Medication that can treat the symptoms of anxiety such as sertraline or citalopram. Depending on the symptoms, the person may need medicine to treat their physical symptoms, as well as their psychological symptoms.

Applied relaxation

Applied relaxation focuses on relaxing muscles in a particular way during situations that usually cause anxiety.

SIGNPOSTING FOR ANXIETY

Anxiety UK
anxietyuk.org.uk
Advice and support for people living with anxiety.

Anxiety Care UK
anxietycare.org.uk
Helps people to recover from anxiety disorders.

Breathing Space
www.breathingspace.scot
A free, confidential phone and web based service for people in Scotland experiencing low mood, depression or anxiety.

Fearfighter
fearfighter.com
A computer-based CBT programme for people who struggle with phobias or feelings of panic or anxiety.

NHS Choices
nhs.uk
Provides a wealth of information on treatments for anxiety available through the NHS.

Rethink Mental Illness
rethink.org
Advice and support for a range of mental health conditions.

Samaritans
samaritans.org
A 24-hour telephone helpline for people struggling to cope.

SAMH - Scottish Association for Mental Health
www.samh.org.uk
Provides a range of mental health support and services.

Post-traumatic stress disorder *(PTSD)* is caused by very stressful, disturbing or frightening events, such as being abused.

PTSD is categorised as an anxiety disorder and people often recall the traumatic incident through nightmares and flashbacks.

PTSD can significantly affect a person's day-to-day life making it very hard to cope. It is estimated that PTSD affects 1 in every 3 people who have experienced a traumatic event.

The causes of post-traumatic stress disorder:

- **Being assaulted or sexually assaulted**
- **Persistent physical, sexual or emotional abuse**
- **Military combat**
- **Terrorist attacks**
- **A traumatic birth**
- **Being kidnapped or held as a hostage**
- **Being raped, mugged or robbed**
- **Witnessing someone being seriously hurt or killed**
- **Losing a relative or a close friend**
- **Being diagnosed with a life-threatening condition**
- **Serious road traffic accidents**
- **Being involved in a natural disaster**

THE SIGNS AND SYMPTOMS OF POST-TRAUMATIC STRESS DISORDER

Re-experiencing:
The most common symptom of PTSD. This is where the individual involuntarily relives the traumatic event in the form of flashbacks, nightmares, repetitive and distressing images or sensations and physical sensations, such as pain and feeling sick.

Avoidance:
The person constantly tries to avoid being reminded of the event. This usually results in avoiding certain people or evading places that remind them of the trauma. This can lead to the person isolating themselves from society and giving up activities they used to enjoy.

Emotional numbing:
Blocking out the traumatic memories completely.

Hyperarousal:
Feeling very anxious and constantly alert to potential threats. This may also be described as feeling 'on edge' and often leads to irritability, outbursts of anger, difficulties sleeping and problems concentrating.

Other possible effects:

- **Drug and alcohol misuse**
- **Self-harming**
- **Aggressive behaviour**
- **Headaches and dizziness**
- **Chest pain and stomach ache**
- **Feelings of hopelessness**

The first aid procedure for post-traumatic stress disorder:

- Keep them safe and give them plenty of time to talk at their own pace. It is important not to pressure them

- Do not dismiss their experiences by saying *"it could have been worse"* or questioning why they didn't say or do something differently

- Don't make assumptions - accept what they say without judging them and show your understanding. Try not to appear shocked or startled by what they tell you

- If this is the first time they have spoken about their problem, assist them to seek initial professional support

- For the interim, you can help them access information and resources relating to their signs and symptoms

- If they have already been given a diagnosis, encourage them to revisit their GP or other assigned professional for additional support such as a peer support group

- People diagnosed with PTSD are often aware of their 'triggers'. Ask them what will make things easier to cope and manage their symptoms

THE TREATMENTS AVAILABLE TO HELP SOMEONE WITH PTSD

Watchful waiting – for mild symptoms of PTSD *(or if a person has been experiencing symptoms for less than 4-weeks)*, 'watchful waiting' may be recommended. This involves monitoring symptoms to see if they improve or get worse. A follow-up appointment will take place within 1-month of the initial appointment.

Trauma based CBT – uses a range of psychological techniques to help people come to terms with the traumatic experience. The therapist may ask the person to confront their traumatic memories by thinking about the experience in detail. The therapist will try to help them gain control of their fear by changing the negative way they think about the experience. Trauma based CBT usually consists of 8-12 weekly one-to-one sessions.

Antidepressants – medication that can treat the symptoms of PTSD *(namely, paroxetine and sertraline)*. Medication will often be provided in conjunction with talking therapies.

Eye movement desensitisation and reprocessing *(EMDR)* – a treatment designed to reduce undesirable thoughts and feelings associated with traumatic memories or events. The treatment involves the person making side-to-side eye movements, usually by following the motion of the therapist's finger, while recalling the traumatic incident. Other methods may include the therapist tapping their finger or playing a tone.

Group therapy – attending group therapy can be an effective method to treat the symptoms of PTSD. People often find it helpful to speak about their experiences with other people who are in a similar position. It can also bring benefits by listening to positive stories of recovery.

SIGNPOSTING FOR POST-TRAUMATIC STRESS DISORDER

ASSIST trauma care
assisttraumacare.org.uk
Information and specialist help for people with PTSD and anyone supporting them.

Combat Stress
combatstress.org.uk
Treatment and support for British Armed Forces Veterans who have mental health problems.

Disaster Action
disasteraction.org.uk
Information and support for people affected by major disasters in the UK and overseas.

NHS Choices
nhs.uk
Provides a wealth of information on treatments for PTSD available through the NHS.

Rape Crisis
rapecrisis.org.uk
Providing a range of services for women and girls who have experienced abuse, domestic violence and sexual assault.

Victim Support
victimsupport.org.uk
Providing support and information to victims or witnesses of crime.

Self-harm is when somebody intentionally damages or injures their body. It's usually a way of coping with, or expressing overwhelming emotional distress.

Sometimes when people self-harm, they feel on some level that they intend to die. More than half of people who die by suicide have a history of self-harm.

But the intention is more often to punish themselves, express their distress, or relieve unbearable tension. Sometimes it's a mixture of all three.

Self-harm can also be a cry for help.

WHY PEOPLE SELF-HARM

Self-harm is more common than many people realise, especially among younger people.

It's estimated around 10% of young people self-harm at some point, but people of all ages do.

This figure is also likely to be an underestimate, as not everyone seeks help.

In most cases, people who self-harm do it to help them cope with overwhelming emotional issues, which may be caused by:

- **Social problems – such as being bullied, having difficulties at work or school, having difficult relationships with friends or family, coming to terms with their sexuality or coping with cultural expectations, such as an arranged marriage**
- **Trauma – such as physical or sexual abuse, the death of a close family member or friend, or having a miscarriage**
- **Psychological causes – such as having repeated thoughts or voices telling them to self-harm, disassociating** (losing touch with who they are and with their surroundings), **or borderline personality disorder**

TYPES OF SELF-HARM

These issues can lead to a build-up of intense feelings of anger, guilt, hopelessness and self-hatred. The individual may not know who to turn to for help and self-harming may become a way to release these pent-up feelings.

Self-harm is linked to anxiety and depression. These mental health conditions can affect people of any age.

Self-harm can also occur alongside antisocial behaviour, such as misbehaving at school or getting into trouble with the police.

Although some people who self-harm are at a high risk of suicide, many people who self-harm do not want to end their lives. In fact, the self-harm may help them cope with emotional distress, so they don't feel the need to kill themselves.

There are many ways people can intentionally harm themselves, such as:

- Cutting, scratching or burning their skin
- Punching, slapping or hitting themselves
- Poisoning themselves with tablets or toxic chemicals
- Misusing alcohol or drugs
- Deliberately starving themselves
- Persistently interfering with wound healing
- Piercing the skin with sharp objects
- Pulling out hair
- Excessively exercising

People often try to keep self-harm a secret because of shame or fear of discovery.

For example, if they're cutting themselves, they may cover up their skin and avoid discussing the problem.

It's often up to close family and friends to notice when somebody is self-harming, and to approach the subject with care and understanding.

Reasons for self-harming

People who self-harm are usually struggling to cope with overwhelming emotional problems or very difficult circumstances. Specific reasons for self-harm may include:

- **Being bullied or having difficult relationships**
- **Alcohol and drug misuse**
- **Psychological causes such as hearing voices telling them to self-harm**
- **Financial worries**

SIGNS OF SELF-HARM

If you think a friend or relative is self-harming, look out for any of the following signs:

- Unexplained cuts, bruises or cigarette burns, usually on their wrists, arms, thighs and chest
- Keeping themselves fully covered at all times, even in hot weather
- Signs of depression, such as low mood, tearfulness or a lack of motivation or interest in anything
- Self-loathing and expressing a wish to punish themselves
- Not wanting to go on and wishing to end it all
- Becoming very withdrawn and not speaking to others
- Changes in eating habits or being secretive about eating, and any unusual weight loss or weight gain
- Signs of low self-esteem, such as blaming themselves for any problems or thinking they're not good enough for something
- Signs they have been pulling out their hair
- Signs of alcohol or drug misuse

People who self-harm can seriously hurt themselves, so it's important that they speak to a GP about the underlying issue and request treatment or therapy that could help them.

THE TREATMENTS AVAILABLE TO HELP SOMEONE WHO SELF-HARMS

If the person's physical injuries are not of a serious nature, the first option is to be book an appointment with their GP. They can assess any previous injuries and scars and recommend further assessments with a specialist.

Their GP will ask questions to see if they have any underlying medical conditions, such as depression or anxiety and treat accordingly. If the person's physical injuries do require treatment in hospital, they will receive the necessary medical treatment and then be referred to a psychiatrist for an assessment before leaving hospital.

Assessments will then take place over several meetings to find out more about their self-harming behaviour. The results of the assessments will be used to help determine the course of treatment and support they need.

Following assessment, any further treatment will usually be jointly decided between the person who self-harms and the healthcare professionals. It will be a specific programme for the individual, according to their needs.

In most cases, talking treatments will be recommended for people who self-harm, such as cognitive behavioural therapy *(CBT)*. This involves attending sessions with a therapist to talk about their thoughts and feelings, and how these affect their behaviour and wellbeing.

If the individual also has mental health problems such as anxiety or depression, their treatment plan may also involve medication, such as antidepressants.

Other recommendations may include specialist treatment for scars, attending peer support groups and self-help techniques.

The first aid procedure for self-harm:

- **Assess the danger and keep yourself safe. Move to a safer place or remove the danger which has caused their injuries**
- **Do not ignore their injuries, or overly focus on them - stay calm**
- **Ask if you can provide first aid, if you are able to do so. Depending on the extent of injury, you may need to call the emergency services**
- **Let the person know that you care for them and you are there to help**
- **Relate to them as a whole person, not just their condition**
- **Once the person is safe from further harm, provide an opportunity for them to talk about their situation. Apply non-judgemental listening skills and show compassion**
- **Offer your support by listening to what they say and let them be in control of their own decisions**
- **Assist the person to obtain professional support if they would like you to, or contact a close friend or family member who they can trust in this situation**

SIGNPOSTING FOR SELF-HARM

Childline
www.childline.org.uk
Online, on the phone, anytime.

Harmless
harmless.org.uk
Provides a range of services for people who self-harm and their friends and families.

Lifesigns
lifesigns.org.uk
User-led self-harm guidance and support network.

Mind
mind.org.uk
Promotes the views and needs of people with mental health problems, including self-harm.

National Self Harm Network
nshn.co.uk
Survivor-led, closely monitored forum for people who self-harm and their friends and families.

NHS Choices
nhs.uk
Provides a wealth of information on treatments for self-harm.

YoungMinds Parents Helpline
youngminds.org.uk
Advice and support helpline for anyone worried about a child or young person under 25.

SUICIDE

SUICIDE IS WHEN SOMEONE DELIBERATELY ENDS THEIR OWN LIFE

'**Suicidal thoughts**' occur when somebody is thinking about, or planning suicide. This could be a momentary thought, through to a detailed plan on how they may take their own life.

Just because someone experiences suicidal emotions it doesn't necessarily mean they will actually go through with it. Suicidal thoughts are common, and many people think about suicide at some point in their lifetime.

People who take their own life have often told someone that they do not feel their life is worth living anymore. Some people may have actually said they want to die. Because of this, it is extremely important to take anybody who talks about feeling suicidal seriously and try to make sure they remain safe.

THE LEGAL HISTORY OF SUICIDE

'Committing suicide' was illegal until 1961, hence the use of the word 'committed'. So, as if life wasn't bad enough, people would also be sent to jail if they failed to take their own life.

However, suicide is no longer a criminal offence and the word 'committed' should not be used, other terminology such as 'completed' or 'attempted' should be used.

Suicide statistics

- **6,556 suicides were registered in 2021**
- **Approximately 74% were male and 26% were female**
- **Males are approximately 3x more likely to die by suicide than females**
- **The highest suicide rate was for men aged 50-54**
- **In the UK, someone takes their own life every 80 minutes**

Reference: Samaritans, Suicide Statistics, 2021

possible risk factors for suicide:

- Previous suicide attempts
- Mental health problems
- Physical, sexual or emotional abuse
- Drug and alcohol misuse/addiction
- Imprisonment
- Bullying and discrimination
- Bereavement or the end of a relationship
- Losing a loved one to suicide
- Adjusting to a significant change
- Being diagnosed with a serious medical condition
- Social isolation and loneliness
- Financial problems or homelessness

E POTENTIAL WARNING SIGNS FOR SUICIDE

ential warning signs that someone is experiencing suicidal thoughts may lude:

- Threatening to hurt or kill themselves
- Talking or writing about dying, death or suicide
- Making financial preparations such as writing or updating a will
- Recent trauma or life crisis such as the death of a loved one
- Talking about feeling hopeless or having no purpose
- Talking about being a burden or nuisance to others
- Anxious, agitated or acting reckless
- Increasing the use of alcohol and drugs
- Withdrawing from activities and feeling isolated

The first aid procedure for suicidal behaviour or emotions:

- **Provide opportunity for the person to talk. If the person does not initiate a conversation with you, you should say something to them**
- **Once the conversation is open, tell the person why you're worried about them and ask about suicide...** *"Have you had thoughts of ending your life?"*
- **Listen to what they say carefully, remain calm and provide reassurance**
- **Phrases such as** *"my life isn't worth living anymore"* **or** *"I just want to disappear"* **must be taken seriously**
- **If you believe the person is in serious danger and they have tried, or are going to try to take their own life, stay with them and call the emergency services**
- **If they are not actively suicidal, encourage them to seek professional support** *(they can book an emergency appointment with their GP in the first instance)*
- **If they are already in touch with specialist mental health services, such as being assigned to a crisis team, they may have a contact number to call when they need support**

Other contact options can include:

- **Trusted friend or family member**
- **NHS 111 service**
- **Samaritans helpline – 116 123**

It can be very emotional helping someone who is feeling suicidal.

However, you must remember that you are helping someone through a very tough time and your conversation could help to save their life.

THE TREATMENTS AVAILABLE TO HELP SOMEONE WHO HAS EXPERIENCED SUICIDAL BEHAVIOURS OR EMOTIONS

It is estimated that 90% of people who attempt or die by suicide have one or more mental health conditions. However, in some cases, the condition may not have been formally diagnosed before the suicidal crisis.

If someone is treated in hospital following a suicidal crisis, they will usually be assessed to find out the best options to keep them safe. This should include a referral to a specialist to organise a professional treatment plan.

When someone visits their GP because of their suicidal emotions, the outcome will be similar to that of the hospital. The GP will assess their condition and work out the most appropriate treatment plan. This could also include being referred to a specialist mental health team (or crisis team).

The treatment plan will be based around the mental health condition the person may be diagnosed with (such as depression or schizophrenia). The treatment plan may consist of talking therapy, interpersonal therapy, group therapy, medication or a combination of these treatment methods and the person may also be referred to a specialist crisis team.

Crisis teams are part of the NHS mental health services and they provide urgent help and support for people going through a mental health crisis. A person who is referred to a crisis team should be given a contact number to call when they need support. 'Crisis team' is a general term and the service may be called something different depending on where you live.

Mental health crisis plan:

An informal care plan outlining key information to be considered during a mental health crisis. By creating a crisis plan, the person is providing important steps to follow when they are in a state of crisis and the plan can be used by the individual themselves or by a friend or family member.

The crisis plan may include:

- **Who to contact** *(trusted friend etc.)*
- **Professional contacts** *(crisis team etc.)*
- **Coping strategies**
- **Their reasons to remain safe and well**
- **Things to avoid when in crisis**
- **Condition history and medication details**

SIGNPOSTING FOR SUICIDE

CALM *(Campaign Against Living Miserably)*
thecalmzone.net
Listening services, information and support for men at risk of suicide.

Maytree Suicide Respite Centre
maytree.org.uk
Offers free respite stays for people in suicidal crisis.

Papyrus HOPELINEUK
papyrus-uk.org
Confidential support for under-35s at risk of suicide and others who are concerned about them.

Samaritans
samaritans.org
Offering emotional support for everyone, 24 hours a day.

Side by Side
sidebyside.mind.org.uk
Mind's supportive online community providing confidential help on mental health problems, including suicide.

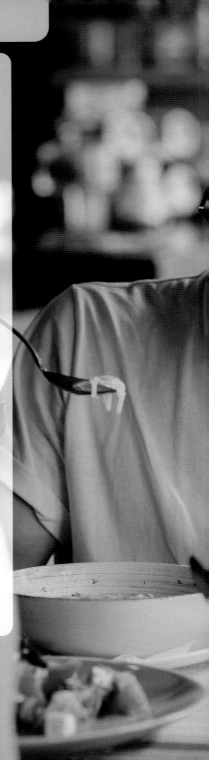

An eating disorder is when someone has an unhealthy attitude towards food which can take over their everyday life and make them feel very poorly.

Food plays an important part in all of our lives and we all spend time thinking about what we have eaten, or what we are going to eat.

When someone has an eating disorder, they will often eat too much or too little and become obsessed with their body weight and appearance.

Many people believe if someone has an eating problem, they will noticeably appear under or overweight – this is not true! Anyone, regardless of their weight, age or gender can be seriously affected by an eating disorder.

TYPES OF EATING DISORDERS

The most common eating disorders are:

- **Anorexia nervosa – when someone tries to keep their bodyweight as low as possible by not eating enough food, exercising too much, or both**

- **Bulimia – when someone eats a lot of food in a very short amount of time** *(bingeing)* **and are then deliberately sick, use laxatives** *(medication to help with their bowel movements),* **restrict what they eat, or do too much exercise to try to stop themselves gaining weight**

- **Binge eating disorder – when someone regularly loses control of their eating, eats large portions of food all at once until they feel uncomfortably full, and are then often upset or guilty**

- **Other specified feeding or eating disorder** *(OSFED)* **– when the symptoms don't exactly match those of anorexia, bulimia or binge eating disorder, but it doesn't mean it is a less serious illness**

WHAT CAN CAUSE EATING DISORDERS?

We don't know exactly what causes eating disorders.

A person may be more likely to get an eating disorder if:

- **They have been criticised for their eating habits, body shape or weight**
- **A family member has a history of eating disorders, depression or a drug addiction**
- **They are involved in a career which promotes being thin and weight loss, such as modelling**
- **They have anxiety, low self-esteem, an obsessive personality, or are a perfectionist**
- **They have been sexually abused or suffered severe trauma in childhood**

WARNING SIGNS OF AN EATING DISORDER

It can often be very difficult to identify that a loved one or friend, has developed an eating disorder.

Warning signs to look out for include:

- **Dramatic weight loss**
- **Lying about how much and when they have eaten, or how much they weigh**
- **Eating a lot of food very fast**
- **Going to the bathroom a lot after eating, often returning looking flushed**
- **Feelings of anxiety about eating or digesting food**
- **Obsessively exercising and sticking to a rigid diet**
- **Cutting food into small pieces or eating very slowly**
- **Avoiding eating with others or eating in secret**
- **Checking body weight and comparing to others**
- **Developing physical health problems**

GETTING HELP FOR SOMEONE WITH AN EATING DISORDER

It can be difficult to know what to do if you are concerned that someone you know has an eating disorder.

People with an eating disorder are often secretive and defensive about their eating and their weight, and they may deny being unwell.

Let them know you are worried about them and encourage them to see their GP.

The first aid procedure for eating disorders:

- If you believe someone may have an eating problem, choose an appropriate time and place to speak to them where you will both feel comfortable and won't be disturbed by others

- Avoid approaching the person before, during or after meal times as this could make them feel uncomfortable and they may not want to talk about their situation

- When the timing is right, tell the person why you are worried in an open and honest manner and ask how they are feeling

- Do not centre the conversation around food or bodyweight as this could make them feel worse

- Show empathy and listen non-judgementally

- Allow the person plenty of time to discuss how they are feeling

- You will need to explain to the person that you think their symptoms indicate a need to seek professional help

- Be aware that the person may react both positively or negatively to your approach. Of course we hope they react positively, but a negative reaction is common and you should not be angry or upset if you're comments are dismissed – you'll be there to help when they feel ready

- Reassure the person that with the right support, they should feel better soon. The individual should be proud of any positive steps already taken, such as acknowledging they have a problem

- Assist and signpost to professional support such as their GP, if it is appropriate. Ask them if they have a trusted family member or friend who can assist and support them

THE TREATMENTS AVAILABLE TO HELP SOMEONE WHO HAS AN EATING DISORDER

It is very difficult for someone to talk about their eating problems, especially with somebody they are not familiar with. However, the sooner they are treated for their condition, the better chance they have of making a full recovery.

The first step should be scheduling an appointment with their GP for an initial health assessment. If the person feels anxious about going alone, they could take a friend or family member along to the appointment for support.

Their GP will ask a series of questions about their eating habits, check their body weight and height and look at the psychological factors of their illness. The GP should then make a referral for the person to see an eating disorder specialist, or a team of specialists for treatment.

Once referred, a healthcare specialist will make a formal assessment and decide on the most appropriate treatment plan for the individual. It is quite common for eating disorders to be diagnosed alongside other conditions, such as anxiety or substance misuse. The specialist will find out if they need any other support and include this within their treatment plan.

The treatment options for eating disorders are very complex and will vary depending on the specific eating disorder the person is diagnosed with.

Generally, treatments can include:

- **Talking treatments** *(such as CBT)*
- **Regular physical health checks**
- **Guided self-help programmes**
- **Peer support groups**
- **Dietary advice and guidance**
- **Medication for related mental health problems**

SIGNPOSTING FOR EATING DISORDERS

Anorexia and Bulimia Care
anorexiabulimiacare.org.uk
Providing on-going care, emotional support and practical guidance for anyone affected by eating disorders.

B-EAT
b-eat.co.uk
Beat is the UK's leading charity supporting anyone affected by eating disorders.

Men Get Eating Disorders Too
mengetedstoo.co.uk
Support and advice for men with eating disorders.

National Centre for Eating Disorders
eating-disorders.org.uk
Everything you need to know about eating disorder treatments, information and professional training.

NHS Choices
nhs.uk/eatingdisorders
Comprehensive information and guidance relating to eating disorders.

Scottish Eating Disorders Interest Group
www.sedig.org
Scotland's charity for supporting, connecting and informing anyone who is affected by eating disorders.

SEED
seedeatingdisorders.org.uk
A group of ordinary people with first-hand experience of eating disorders.

The term 'personality' refers to the group of characteristics that we all develop as we grow up. This includes ways that we THINK, FEEL and BEHAVE. Our personality traits usually stay very similar throughout our lives.

Someone with a personality disorder thinks, feels, behaves or relates to others very differently from the average person and their personality does not necessarily remain consistent and stable.

The symptoms of personality disorders can have such an impact on day-to-day life.

People may find that they develop other mental health problems such as depression, anxiety or substance misuse.

THE TYPES AND CATEGORIES OF PERSONALITY DISORDERS

Personality disorders can be divided into three main clusters according to the psychological characteristics. Someone can have the characteristics of more than one personality disorder.

Categories of personality disorder:

A: Odd or Eccentric	B: Dramatic, Emotional or Erratic	C: Anxious and Fearful
Paranoid	Antisocial or dissocial	Obsessive/Compulsive
Schizoid	Borderline	Avoidant
Schizotypal	Histrionic	Dependent
	Narcissistic	

THE CHARACTERISTICS OF PERSONALITY DISORDERS

Cluster A: Odd or eccentric

- **Paranoid** – irrational suspicion, tend to hold grudges, interpret other people's motivations as malicious
- **Schizoid** – lack of interest in things, social isolation, prefers own company, restricted emotional expression
- **Schizotypal** – discomfort interacting with others, distorted thoughts and perceptions, eccentric behaviour

Cluster B: Dramatic, Emotional and Erratic

- **Antisocial, or Dissocial** – easily frustrated, impulsive, irresponsible, disregard for other people's rights, no guilt
- **Borderline** – unpredictable, difficulty controlling emotions, fears of abandonment and isolation, fluctuating moods
- **Histrionic** – dramatic, over-reactions, changing emotions, self-centred, attention seeking, easily influenced by others
- **Narcissistic** – self-importance, superior to others, arrogant, dreams of success, crave attention, envious of others

Cluster C: Anxious and Fearful

- **Obsessive-Compulsive** – perfectionist, rule-bound lifestyle, sticks to routines, restrained and rigid, desire to be in control, sensitive to criticism, conscientious
- **Avoidant or anxious** – very anxious and tense, hesitant, self-conscious, insecure, have to be liked or accepted, extremely sensitive of what others think about them
- **Dependent** – seek constant reassurance from others, submissive, a need to be taken care of by others, lack of self-confidence, fear of being abandoned

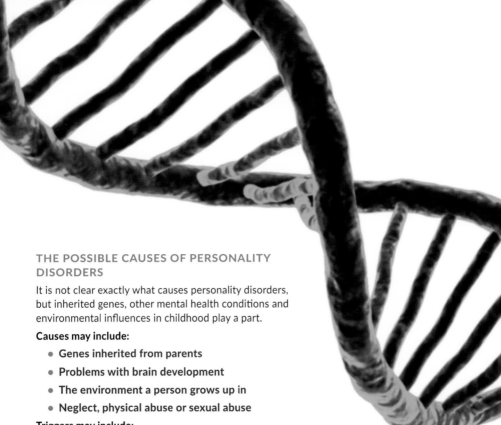

THE POSSIBLE CAUSES OF PERSONALITY DISORDERS

It is not clear exactly what causes personality disorders, but inherited genes, other mental health conditions and environmental influences in childhood play a part.

Causes may include:

- **Genes inherited from parents**
- **Problems with brain development**
- **The environment a person grows up in**
- **Neglect, physical abuse or sexual abuse**

Triggers may include:

- **Mental health problems, incl. drug misuse**
- **Significant life events**
- **Relationship problems**
- **The death of a loved one**

The first aid procedure for personality disorders:

- If a person is experiencing a crisis because of their personality disorder, maintain a calm and non-threatening attitude
- Listen to what they say carefully, make eye contact, provide reassurance and be patient
- Accept what they say without judging them and try to show your understanding of their points of view
- Remind them of the positives you see in them
- You may find that simply talking to them and showing you care can help bring them out of the current crisis
- You may not be aware the person has a personality disorder. In this situation, follow the first aid action plan for mental health – C.A.R.E. and seek support accordingly
- If they have already been given a diagnosis, they should have a telephone number to call, such as a local crisis resolution team *(CRT)* who will be able to help them

THE TREATMENTS AVAILABLE TO HELP SOMEONE WHO HAS A PERSONALITY DISORDER

People often assume that our personalities cannot be changed or rehabilitated, but this is not true. With professional support and the appropriate treatment plan, it is possible for things to change and improve for people with personality disorders.

Professional treatment plans will vary depending on the specific diagnosis of personality disorder. Usually the person is assigned to a community mental health team *(CMHT)* to provide day-to-day support and treatment, while ensuring the person has as much independence as possible.

The treatments described below are based on the most common type of personality disorder – borderline personality disorder *(BPD)*.

Dialectical behaviour therapy *(DBT)* – uses a combination of cognitive and behavioural therapy, with the aim of breaking the vicious cycle of experiencing intense and upsetting emotions, yet feeling guilty and worthless for having these emotions. DBT is based on teamwork with the person expected to work with their therapist and the other people in the group sessions to help combat their strong and distressing emotions collectively.

Therapeutic communities *(TC's)* – structured environments where people with a range of complex psychological conditions come together to interact and take part in group and individual therapy, as well as other activities designed to improve their social skills and self-confidence.

Mentalisation-based therapy *(MBT)* – 'Mentalisation' is the ability to think about thinking. This consists of the person examining their own thoughts and beliefs and assessing whether they're useful, realistic and based on reality. The person learns to hold back from their thoughts about themselves and to examine others to see if their thoughts are valid.

Arts therapies – arts *(or creative therapies)* aim to help people who find it hard to express their thoughts and feelings verbally. The therapy focuses on creating something as a way of expressing their feelings.

Medication – no medication is currently approved to treat BPD, but certain medications are prescribed to treat related mental health conditions. Antipsychotics and mood stabilisers are sometimes prescribed to alleviate psychotic symptoms and to reduce impulsive behaviours.

SIGNPOSTING FOR PERSONALITY DISORDERS

Mind
mind.org.uk
Provides a wealth of information and advice relating to personality disorders.

National Institute for Health and Care Excellence
nice.org.uk
Produces guidelines on best practice in health care, including recommended treatments for Borderline Personality Disorder *(BPD)*.

NHS Choices
nhs.uk
Provides information on personality disorders and treatments which are available through the NHS.

The National Association for People Abused in Childhood *(NAPAC)*
napac.org.uk
A charity supporting adult survivors of any form of childhood abuse. Provides a support line and local support services.

BIPOLAR DISORDER

Bipolar disorder, formerly known as manic depression, is a condition that affects people's moods, which can swing from one extreme to another.

People with bipolar disorder have periods or episodes of:

- **Depression** – feeling very low and lethargic
- **Hypomania and mania** – feeling very high and overactive

  Hypomania – a milder version of mania which lasts for a short period

  Mania – more severe symptoms than hypomania and lasts for a longer period

CAUSES OF BIPOLAR DISORDER

The exact cause of bipolar disorder is unknown, but experts believe there could be a number of combined factors which make a person more susceptible to develop the condition.

Chemical imbalance in the brain – there's evidence to suggest that symptoms of bipolar disorder could be caused by an imbalance in neurotransmitters, which are the chemicals responsible for controlling the brain's functions.

Genetics – bipolar disorder could also be linked to genetics, where family members of a person with the condition have an increased risk in developing it themselves. However, no single gene is responsible for bipolar disorder. Instead, a number of genetic and environmental factors are thought to act as triggers.

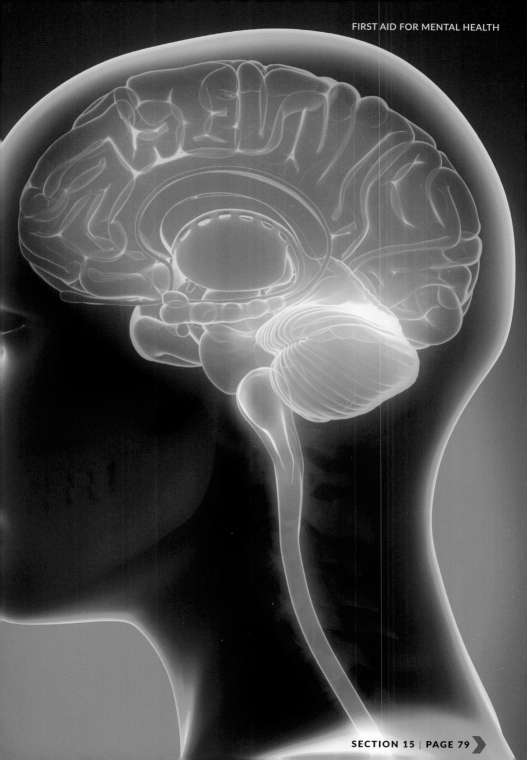

THE SIGNS AND SYMPTOMS OF BIPOLAR DISORDER

During a period of depression, symptoms may include:

- Feeling sad and hopelessness
- Difficulty in concentrating
- Loss of interest in activities
- Feelings of guilt and despair
- Difficulties with sleeping
- Suicidal thoughts

The manic phase of bipolar disorder may include:

- Feeling very happy and elated
- Talking quickly and full of energy
- Easily agitated or irritated
- Doing things with disastrous consequences
- Saying things out of character
- Delusions and hallucinations

The first aid procedure for bipolar disorder:

- If a person is experiencing a depressive or manic episode, stay calm and move to a safer, quieter setting if it is necessary
- The person may say or do things that could be hurtful or embarrassing and these actions should not be taken personally
- Do not tell them they are wrong or that they are making it up – at this moment in time they truly believe what they are saying is real
- Communicate with them clearly, ask simple questions and listen non-judgementally
- If they are experiencing severe symptoms during the episode, they may have a Crisis Plan which you can refer to, or a preferred contact number to call
- If you believe the safety of the person or others is in critical danger, call the emergency services

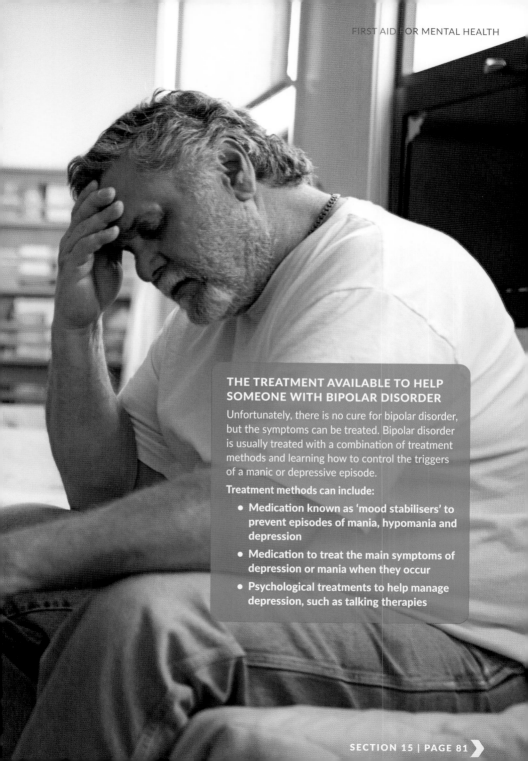

THE TREATMENT AVAILABLE TO HELP SOMEONE WITH BIPOLAR DISORDER

Unfortunately, there is no cure for bipolar disorder, but the symptoms can be treated. Bipolar disorder is usually treated with a combination of treatment methods and learning how to control the triggers of a manic or depressive episode.

Treatment methods can include:

- **Medication known as 'mood stabilisers' to prevent episodes of mania, hypomania and depression**
- **Medication to treat the main symptoms of depression or mania when they occur**
- **Psychological treatments to help manage depression, such as talking therapies**

Medication:

Lithium carbonate – 'lithium' is the most common medication used to treat bipolar disorder and is a long-term method of treatment to control episodes of mania, hypomania and depression.

Anticonvulsant medicine – primarily prescribed to treat the condition epilepsy, but they're also effective in treating the symptoms of bipolar disorder. Anticonvulsant medicines are used to treat episodes of mania and are also long-term mood stabilisers.

Antipsychotic medicines – prescribed to treat episodes of mania or hypomania. Antipsychotic medicines can be particularly useful if symptoms are severe or behaviour is disturbed. May also be used to treat the symptoms of long-term bipolar disorder. Antidepressants are commonly used alongside a stabiliser or antipsychotic to treat depression.

Psychological treatments:

Psychoeducation – involves teaching people specific skills to learn how to recognise the early warning signs of an episode and to learn more about the condition in general.

Cognitive behavioural therapy *(CBT)* – a talking therapy to help manage their thoughts, perceptions, behaviours and coping techniques.

Family therapy – a talking therapy which focuses on family relationships and encourages everyone to work together within the family to improve their understanding of the condition.

SIGNPOSTING FOR BIPOLAR DISORDER

Bipolar UK
bipolaruk.org
Support for people with bipolar disorder and their families and friends.

National Institute for Health and Clinical Excellence (NICE)
nice.org.uk
National guidelines on treatments for bipolar disorder.

NHS Choices
nhs.uk
Provides information on treatments for bipolar disorder available through the NHS.

Rethink
rethink.org
A charity which provides advice, information and services for a range of mental health conditions.

Royal College of Psychiatrists
rcpsych.ac.uk
The professional medical body responsible for supporting psychiatrists.

SANE
sane.org.uk
A forum which allows people to share their feelings and provide mutual support to anyone with mental health problems.

Psychosis is a mental health problem that causes people to perceive or interpret things differently from those around them. This might involve hallucinations or delusions.

Psychosis can be a symptom of several mental health conditions:

Hallucinations – where a person hears, sees and, in some cases, feels, smells or tastes things that aren't there; a common hallucination is hearing voices.

Delusions – where a person has strong beliefs that aren't shared by others; a common delusion is someone believing there is a conspiracy to harm them.

Confused thoughts – confusing speech. Switching from one subject to another mid-sentence. Talking very fast. Sudden loss in their train of thought.

CAUSES OF PSYCHOSIS

People may experience episodes of psychosis if they have:

Bipolar disorder – when someone experiences episodes of mania *(elated mood)*, they may also experience symptoms of psychosis.

Schizophrenia – a mental health condition which causes hallucinations and delusions.

Substance misuse – alcohol or drug misuse can trigger psychotic episodes, particularly if someone stops using substances after a long period of time *(withdrawal symptoms)*.

Postpartum psychosis – a rare but serious mental health illness which can happen to any woman following childbirth. 1:500 women are affected by postpartum psychosis.

Medical conditions, anxiety, depression or a lack of sleep.

The first aid procedure for psychosis:

- **If you believe someone is experiencing symptoms of psychosis, approach them with a calm and caring attitude**
- **Choose an appropriate time and place where you will both feel comfortable**
- **The person may be very frightened about what they are experiencing and worry what other people may think about them**
- **Share your concerns with them, listen to what they say without judgement and show that you are there to support them**
- **The person may say things out of character which you may find unusual – do not dismiss what they say or try and correct the person**
- **You should ask them if they have felt this way before. If they are already receiving treatment, ask them what helps them in this situation** *(e.g. contacting a family member)*
- **If they are experiencing a severe psychotic episode, the person should go to hospital. Call the emergency services for assistance**

THE TREATMENTS AVAILABLE TO HELP SOMEONE WITH PSYCHOSIS

If the person is taken to A&E, they will be seen by a psychiatric doctor to assess their condition.

Treatment for psychosis will vary depending on the underlying cause, but will usually involve a combination of antipsychotic medicines, psychological therapies and social support.

People who experience an episode of psychosis for the first time will be referred to an 'early intervention team' who will make an assessment of their needs and work out the most appropriate treatment plan.

Antipsychotics – most people with psychosis will be prescribed antipsychotic medication in the first instance, such as 'olanzapine'. Antipsychotics work by blocking the effect of dopamine, a chemical that transmits messages in the brain.

Cognitive behavioural therapy *(CBT)* – CBT can help people understand and comprehend their experiences (or episodes) better. The aim of CBT for psychosis is to help deal with their problems in a more positive way by breaking them down into smaller parts. CBT usually consists of several weekly sessions depending on the severity of the person's symptoms.

Family intervention – family intervention therapy involves a series of meetings that take place over a period of three months or more, to explore ways to help the person with psychosis and how to manage future episodes.

SIGNPOSTING FOR PSYCHOSIS

Hearing Voices network
hearing-voices.org
Information and support for people who
hear voices and local support groups.

**National Institute for Health and Care
Excellence (NICE)**
nice.org.uk
Guidelines on professional treatments
for psychosis.

National Paranoia Network
nationalparanoianetwork.org
Information and support for people who
experience paranoid thoughts.

Royal College of Psychiatrists
rcpsych.ac.uk
The professional medical body
responsible for supporting psychiatrists.

Voice Collective
voicecollective.co.uk
Supports children and young people who
experience psychotic symptoms and
offer support for their families.

Young Minds
youngminds.org.uk
Support for young people affected by
mental health, including psychosis.

Schizophrenia is a long-term mental health disorder that affects how people think, feel and behave. Schizophrenia causes a range of different psychological symptoms and is often described as a type of psychosis because of the similarities in symptoms.

The condition affects approximately 1 in every 100 people in the UK at some point during their life and both men and women can equally be affected.

Some people think schizophrenia causes a 'split personality' or makes people violent and aggressive – this is not true. Violent or dangerous behaviour is usually caused by the misuse of alcohol or drugs.

THE POSSIBLE CAUSES OF SCHIZOPHRENIA

The specific cause of schizophrenia is unknown but evidence suggests it is a combination of factors which makes someone more susceptible to develop the condition.

Genetics – someone is more likely to develop schizophrenia if they have a close family member such as a parent who has the condition, but no single gene is thought to be responsible.

As well as genetic factors, schizophrenia may be caused by:

Problems with brain development – studies have shown people with schizophrenia have slight differences in the structure of the brain.

Neurotransmitters – an imbalance in the level of neurotransmitters *(dopamine and serotonin)* which carry messages between brain cells.

Pregnancy complications – people who develop schizophrenia are more likely to have experienced complications before and during their birth, such as premature labour, or a lack of oxygen during birth.

Triggers for people at risk – Stressful events such as bereavement, divorce or physical and sexual abuse can trigger the condition.

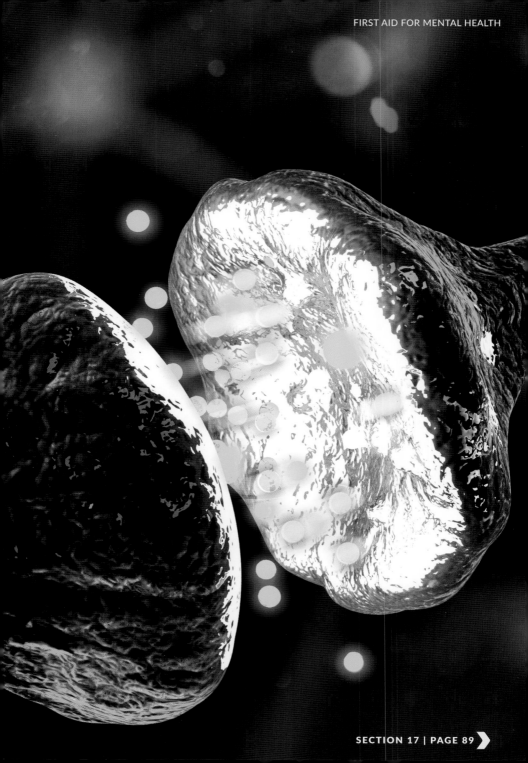

THE SIGNS AND SYMPTOMS OF SCHIZOPHRENIA

The symptoms of schizophrenia are usually classified into:

Positive symptoms – any change in behaviour or thoughts, such as hallucinations or delusions.

Negative symptoms – a withdrawal or lack of function that you would not usually expect to see in a healthy person; for example, people with schizophrenia often appear emotionless and flat.

'Positive' symptoms:

- **Hallucinations**
- **Delusions**
- **Confused thoughts**
- **Behavioural changes**

'Negative' symptoms:

- **Social withdrawal and isolation**
- **Loss of motivation and concentration**
- **Changes in sleeping patterns**
- **Not caring about hygiene or appearance**

THE FIRST AID PROCEDURE FOR SCHIZOPHRENIA
(similar to psychosis):

- **If you believe someone is experiencing symptoms of schizophrenia, approach them with a calm and caring attitude**
- **Choose an appropriate time and place where you will both feel comfortable**
- **The person may be very frightened about what they are experiencing and worry what other people may think about them**
- **Share your concerns with them, listen to what they say without judgement and show that you are there to support them**
- **The person may say things out of character which you may find unusual – do not dismiss what they say or try and correct the person**
- **You should ask them if they have felt this way before. If they are already receiving treatment, ask them what helps them in this situation** *(for e.g. contacting a family member)*
- **If they are experiencing severe psychotic symptoms, the person should go to hospital. Call the emergency services for assistance**

THE AVAILABLE TREATMENT TO HELP SOMEONE WITH SCHIZOPHRENIA

As with psychosis, when someone experiences symptoms of schizophrenia for the first time, they will be referred to an 'early intervention team' so they can make an assessment of their needs and work out the most appropriate treatment plan. People with complex needs will be entered into a 'care programme approach' which consists of four stages:

1 **Assessment – the person's condition will be formally assessed.**

2 **Care plan – a care plan is created based on the outcome of the assessment.**

3 **Key worker – a professional will be appointed as the first point of contact.**

4 **Review – the person's treatment plan will be reviewed at regular intervals.**

Medication – antipsychotics are usually prescribed to reduce the symptoms of schizophrenia, but they do not cure the illness.

Cognitive behavioural therapy *(CBT)* – CBT can help the person identify their thinking patterns that are causing the unwanted feelings and behaviours, and helps them learn how to replace this thinking with more realistic and useful thoughts.

Family therapy – many people with schizophrenia have to rely on other people for care and support and this can often place a strain on relationships. Family therapy helps to reduce any problems in the family caused by the persons symptoms.

Arts therapy – a non-verbal treatment method which allows the person to express their feelings and experiences of schizophrenia creatively, and has been shown to alleviate the symptoms.

SIGNPOSTING FOR SCHIZOPHRENIA

Hearing Voices network
hearing-voices.org
Information and support for people who hear voices and local support groups.

Living With Schizophrenia
livingwithschizophreniauk.org
A charity website managed by people with personal experiences of the condition.

National Paranoia Network
nationalparanoianetwork.org
Information and support for people who experience paranoid thoughts.

SANE
sane.org.uk
A forum which allows people to share their feelings and provide mutual support to anyone with mental health problems.

Voice collective
voicecollective.co.uk
Supports children and young people who experience psychotic symptoms and offer support for their families.

Young Minds
youngminds.org.uk
Support for young people affected by mental health, including psychosis.

MENTAL HEALTH HELPLINES

Whether you're concerned about yourself, a friend or a loved one, these helplines and support groups can offer expert advice.

Anxiety UK
Charity providing support for people affected by anxiety disorders.
Phone: 03444 775 774 *(Mon to Fri, 9.30am to 5.30pm)*
Website: www.anxietyuk.org.uk

Bipolar UK
A charity helping people living with manic depression or bipolar disorder.
Website: www.bipolaruk.org.uk

Breathing Space
A free, confidential phone and web based service for people in Scotland experiencing low mood, depression or anxiety.
Phone: 0800 83 85 87 *(Mon to Thurs, 6pm to 2am. Fri to Mon, 6pm to 6am)*
Website: www.breathingspace.scot

CALM
CALM is the Campaign Against Living Miserably, for men aged 15 to 35.
Phone: 0800 58 58 58 *(daily, 5pm to midnight)*
Website: www.thecalmzone.net

Childline
Online, on the phone, anytime.
Phone: 0800 1111 *(24-hour service)*
Website: www.childline.org.uk

Men's Health Forum
24/7 stress support for men by text, chat and email.
Website: www.menshealthforum.org.uk

Mental Health Foundation
Provides information and support for anyone with mental health problems or learning disabilities.
Website: www.mentalhealth.org.uk

Mind
Promotes the views and needs of people with mental health problems.
Phone: 0300 123 3393 *(Mon to Fri, 9am to 6pm)*
Website: www.mind.org.uk

No Panic
Voluntary charity offering support for sufferers of panic attacks and obsessive compulsive disorder *(OCD)*. Offers a course to help overcome phobias and OCD.
Phone: 0844 967 4848 *(daily, 10am to 10pm)*
Website: www.nopanic.org.uk

OCD Action
Support for people with OCD. Includes information on treatment and online resources.
Phone: 0845 390 6232 *(Mon to Fri, 9.30am to 5pm)*
Website: www.ocdaction.org.uk

OCD UK
A charity run by people with OCD, for people with OCD. Includes facts, news and treatments.
Phone: 0845 120 3778 *(Mon to Fri, 9am to 5pm)*
Website: www.ocduk.org

PAPYRUS
Young suicide prevention society.
Phone: HOPElineUK 0800 068 4141 *(Mon to Fri, 10am to 5pm & 7 to 10pm. Weekends 2 to 5pm)*
Website: www.papyrus-uk.org

Rethink Mental Illness
Support and advice for people living with mental illness.
Phone: 0300 5000 927 *(Mon to Fri, 9.30am to 4pm)*
Website: www.rethink.org

Samaritans
Confidential support for people experiencing feelings of distress or despair.
Phone: 116 123 *(free 24-hour helpline)*
Website: www.samaritans.org.uk

SAMH - Scottish Association for Mental Health
Provides a range of mental health support and services
Phone: 0141 530 1000 *(Mon to Fri, 9am to 5pm)*
Website: www.samh.org.uk

SANE
Emotional support, information and guidance for people affected by mental illness, their families and carers.
SANEline: 0300 304 7000 *(daily, 4.30 to 10.30pm)*
Textcare: comfort and care via text message, sent when the person needs it most:
                http://www.sane.org.uk/textcare
Peer support forum: www.sane.org.uk/supportforum
Website: www.sane.org.uk/support

YoungMinds
Information on child and adolescent mental health. Services for parents and professionals.
Phone: Parents' helpline 0808 802 5544 *(Mon to Fri, 9.30am to 4pm)*
Website: www.youngminds.org.uk

ABUSE (CHILD, SEXUAL, DOMESTIC VIOLENCE)

NSPCC
Children's charity dedicated to ending child abuse and child cruelty.
Phone: 0800 1111 for Childline for children *(24-hour helpline)*
                0808 800 5000 for adults concerned about a child *(24-hour helpline)*
Website: www.nspcc.org.uk

Refuge
Advice on dealing with domestic violence.
Phone: 0808 2000 247 *(24-hour helpline)*
Website: www.refuge.org.uk

ADDICTION (DRUGS, ALCOHOL, GAMBLING)

Alcoholics Anonymous
Phone: 0845 769 7555 *(24-hour helpline)*
Website: www.alcoholics-anonymous.org.uk

Gamblers Anonymous
Website: www.gamblersanonymous.org.uk

Narcotics Anonymous
Phone: 0300 999 1212 *(daily 10am to midnight)*
Website: www.ukna.org

ALZHEIMER'S

Alzheimer's Society
Provides information on dementia, including factsheets and helplines.

Phone: 0300 222 1122 *(Mon to Fri, 9am to 5pm. Weekends, 10am to 4pm)*
Website: www.alzheimers.org.uk

BEREAVEMENT

Cruse Bereavement Care
Phone: 0844 477 9400 *(Mon to Fri, 9am to 5pm)*
Website: www.crusebereavementcare.org.uk

CRIME VICTIMS

Rape Crisis
To find your local services phone: 0808 802 9999 *(daily, 12 to 2.30pm, 7 to 9.30pm)*
Website: www.rapecrisis.org.uk

Victim Support
Phone: 0808 168 9111 *(24-hour helpline)*
Website: www.victimsupport.org

EATING DISORDERS

Beat
Phone: 0808 801 0677 *(adults)* or 0808 801 0711 *(for under-18s)*
Website: www.b-eat.co.uk

LEARNING DISABILITIES

Mencap
Charity working with people with a learning disability, their families and carers.
Phone: 0808 808 1111 *(Mon to Fri, 9am to 5pm)*
Website: www.mencap.org.uk

PARENTING

Family Lives
Advice on all aspects of parenting including dealing with bullying.
Phone: 0808 800 2222 *(Mon to Fri, 9am to 9pm. Sat to Sun, 10am to 3pm)*
Website: www.familylives.org.uk

RELATIONSHIPS

Relate
The UK's largest provider of relationship support.
Website: www.relate.org.uk

MANAGING WORKPLACE STRESS AND MENTAL HEALTH ISSUES

HSE
Website: www.hse.gov.uk/stress/mental-health